Once upon a time there were two bears.

One day the bears were playing
in a tree.

Inside the tree was a bees' nest.

The bears looked inside the nest.

They saw some lovely, runny honey,
but they did not see the bee.

'We can eat the honey,'
said the bears.

'Yum, yum!'

'No, no, no!' said the bee.
'You cannot eat the honey.'

4

'Yes, we can eat the honey,'
said the bears.

'No, you will not!'
said the bee.

'Help! Help!' said the bears.

splash!